Where is Happiness Found?

Paul Franklin, illustrations by Elena Priestley

I am only as high as a grasshopper's knee,
I spend time with my Dad who looks after me.

He shows me all sorts of things, gentle and kind,
And when we're together all beauty we find.

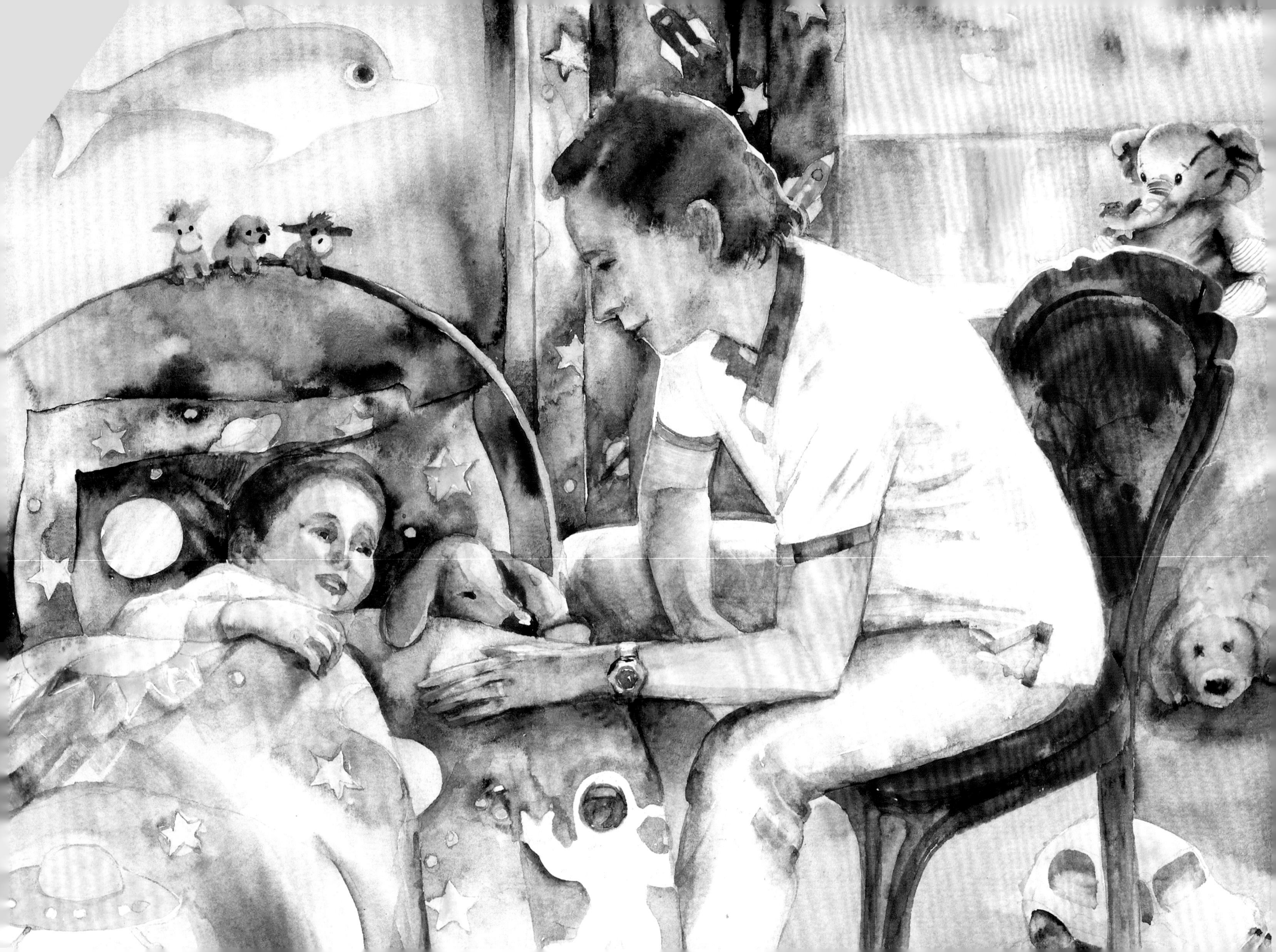

He read me a story then tucked me in bed,
Suddenly a question popped into my head.
"Dad," I asked, "WHERE IS HAPPINESS FOUND?"
He thought for a moment not making a sound!

"It's really simple." He gave me a wink,
And I listened so hard, barely able to blink.
"Are you lying comfortably?" I nodded. "Then I'll start!"
And he told me these secrets, which came from his heart.

"Happiness is always there, you don't have to wait,
But it won't just land at your feet or fall onto your plate.
It isn't like a bus that will come to pick you up,
You don't have to trust your fate or any type of luck.

Imagine riding a carousel horse galloping through the air,
Or getting caught in a thunderstorm — don't give a single care!

Taste a cloud of candy floss spun around a stick,
Pull a rabbit from a hat in a magic trick.

Imagine listening to the wind whistling through the leaves,
Look at tiny acorns which sprout up into trees.
Or hear a tweeting morning bird that pecks a worm then sings,
As if he's found a treasure chest of jewels and golden rings.

Imagine birthday candles all alight upon your cake,
Then blow hard to make the wish you dearly want to make.
Have a flitter flutter butterfly settle on your hand.
Wouldn't that be wonderful? Wouldn't that be grand?

Imagine fairies on your pillow coming to take your tooth,
Hear pitter-patter raindrops as they land upon your roof.

Catch a falling snowflake, let it land upon your tongue,
Feel the seasons come and go, changing warmth of Sun.

Imagine you're at the beach licking ice cream from a cone,
Build castles made of golden sand, for mermaids it's their home.
Watch the waves of the sea whilst eating fish and chips,
Have sugar coated doughnuts trying not to lick your lips.

FE75
FE25

Imagine a little harbour with lots of bobbing boats,
Lobster pots and anchors, fishing nets and floats.
Hold on tightly to the string of a flying kite,
Let it drift and swoop and loop the loop to everyone's delight.

Imagine staring at the Moon at night or towards a twinkling star,
For I am always by your side — I'm never very far!
Swim freely with a dolphin, take a moment to suppose:
You cupped her face between your hands, and gently kissed her nose.

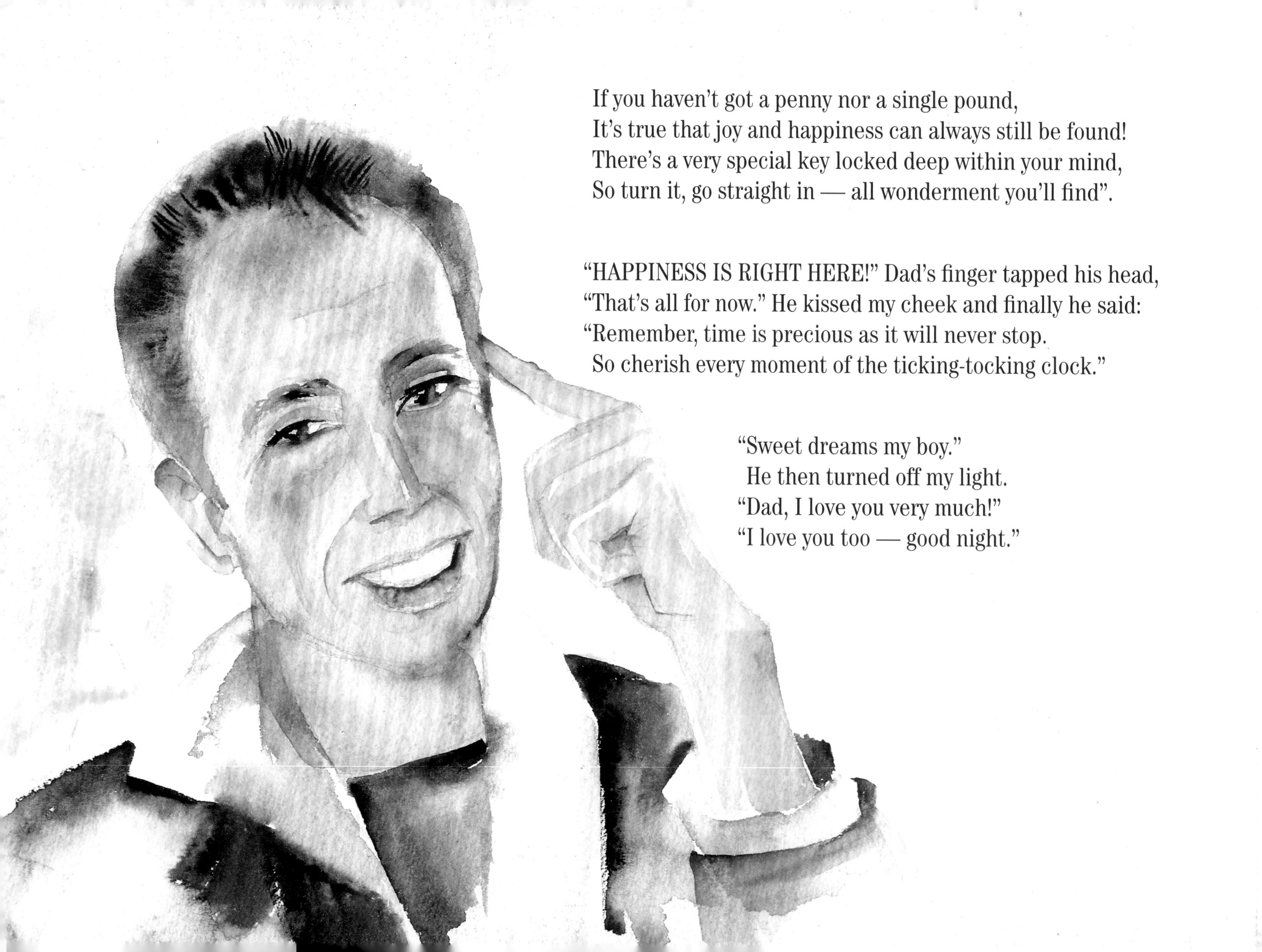

If you haven't got a penny nor a single pound,
It's true that joy and happiness can always still be found!
There's a very special key locked deep within your mind,
So turn it, go straight in — all wonderment you'll find".

"HAPPINESS IS RIGHT HERE!" Dad's finger tapped his head,
"That's all for now." He kissed my cheek and finally he said:
"Remember, time is precious as it will never stop.
So cherish every moment of the ticking-tocking clock."

"Sweet dreams my boy."
He then turned off my light.
"Dad, I love you very much!"
"I love you too — good night."